Japanese patterns to color

Illustrated by Dinara Mirtalipova
Design and cover illustration by Emily Beevers
Written by Laura Cowan

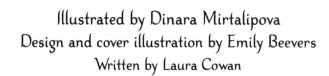

Japanese patterns and colors

For thousands of years, Japanese artists have been covering clothing, pottery and paintings in delicate, colorful patterns. The patterns often come from nature, with different flowers, birds, and trees – and colors – standing for different things.

Japanese people believe cranes bring good luck and a long life.

Carp stand for courage and good luck. They're also the symbol of traditional Japanese warriors called *samurai*.

Blue is thought to be calming.

Waves mean power and strength.

Green stands for nature and peace.

Red stands for life and the Sun.

Chrysanthemums symbolize courage, dignity and strength.

Colorful ceramics

Ceramics, or pottery, is one of the oldest Japanese art forms. Vases, pots and tea sets are decorated with all kinds of patterns – from intricate, bright floral designs to simple geometric patterns on a white background.

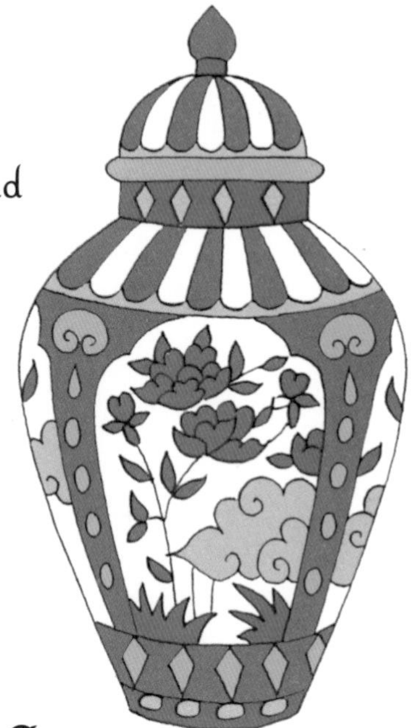

This vase is decorated in a style called *Kinrande Imari*, which uses only red, blue and gold paint to create patterns.

Traditional clothing

Kimono, meaning "thing to wear", is a traditional Japanese robe. There are different styles and patterns for every season, month and festival.

This is a wedding *kimono* named an *uchikake*. It's decorated with symbols and colors that stand for good luck and a long, happy life.

Woodblock printing

From the 17th to the 19th centuries, *Ukiyo-e* was a popular decorative art made by printing pictures using carved blocks of wood. These prints represented everyday scenes or stories.

Graceful geishas

Geishas, or *geikos*, are traditional Japanese female entertainers who wear ornate clothing and accessories. They have to train for many years.

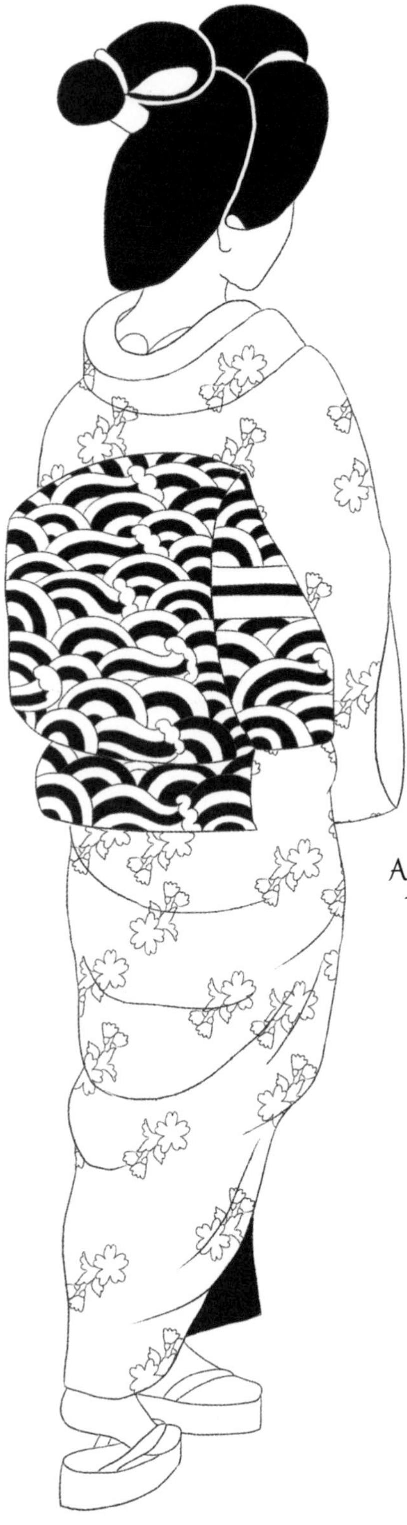

An *obi* is a type of sash. This one is decorated with blue waves.

This *geisha's kimono* is decorated with pink *sakura* (cherry blossom) patterns.

Trainee *geishas* are named *maikos.* They have more elaborate and colorful hair, makeup and clothing than *geishas*, and collars lined with red silk.

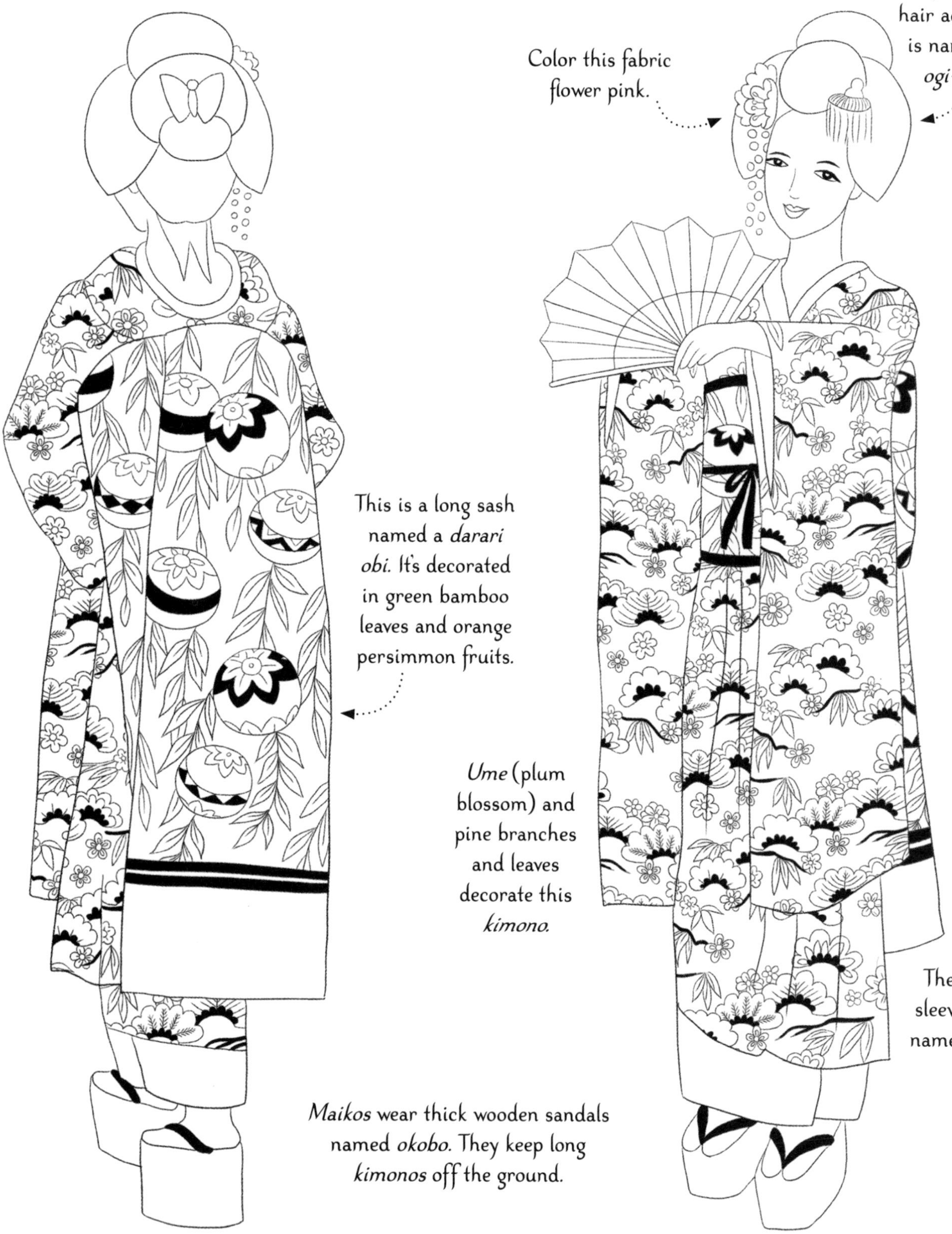

Color this fabric flower pink.

This fan-shaped hair accessory is named an *ogi-bira.*

This is a long sash named a *darari obi.* It's decorated in green bamboo leaves and orange persimmon fruits.

Ume (plum blossom) and pine branches and leaves decorate this *kimono.*

The long sleeves are named *furi.*

Maikos wear thick wooden sandals named *okobo*. They keep long *kimonos* off the ground.

Tea ceremony

Tea ceremonies are an important part of Japanese culture. They involve the preparation and serving of *matcha* (powdered green tea) to guests using special kettles and tea sets.

This kettle is decorated with chrysanthemums and gold *karakusa* (vine leaves) on a blue background.

On the opposite page, a tea server uses a *hishaku* (tea ladle) to pour hot water into tea bowls.

Tea pot painted in gold, red, and blue patterns

Tea bowl

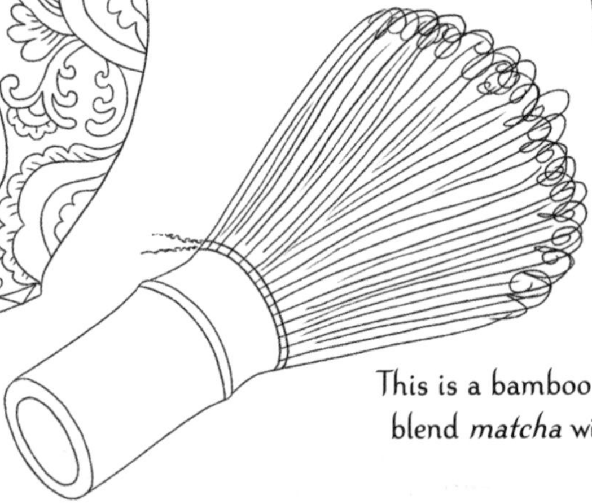

This is a bamboo whisk, used to blend *matcha* with hot water.

Kimonos

Kimonos can be worn by men, women or children and made from any fabric. They are always wrapped around the wearer's body from left to right, then tied with an *obi* (sash).

This fan, covered in a blue flower called *asagao*, is for summer festivals.

Long hair sticks, decorated with fluttering metal strips and flowers

Long-sleeved *kimonos* are named *furisodes*, which means "swinging sleeves".

Color the trailing wisteria pattern purple.

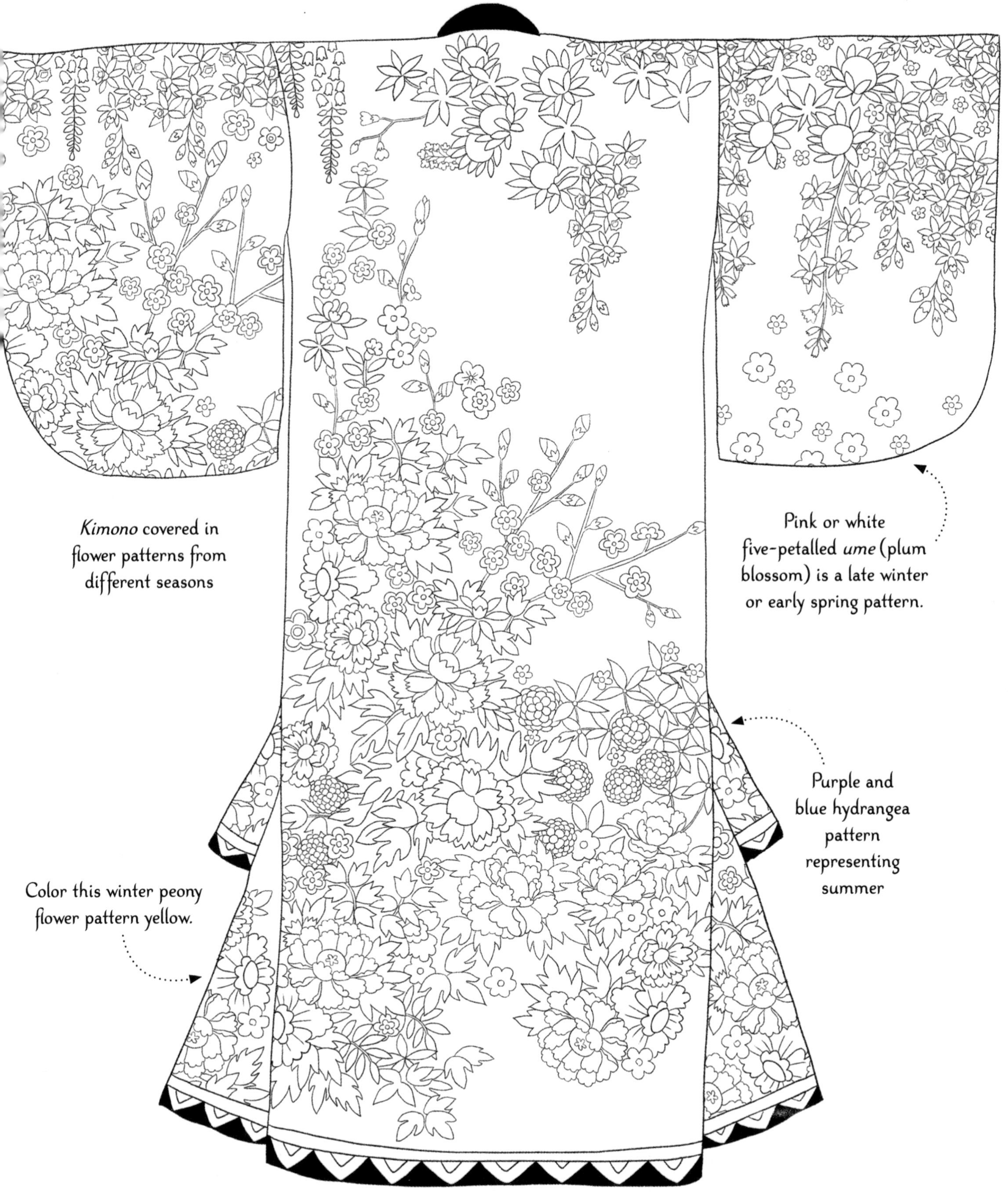
Kimono covered in flower patterns from different seasons
Pink or white five-petalled *ume* (plum blossom) is a late winter or early spring pattern.
Purple and blue hydrangea pattern representing summer
Color this winter peony flower pattern yellow.

Umbrellas

Umbrellas or *wagasa* were introduced to Japan from China over a thousand years ago. They're made from bamboo and oiled paper to keep the rain from soaking through.

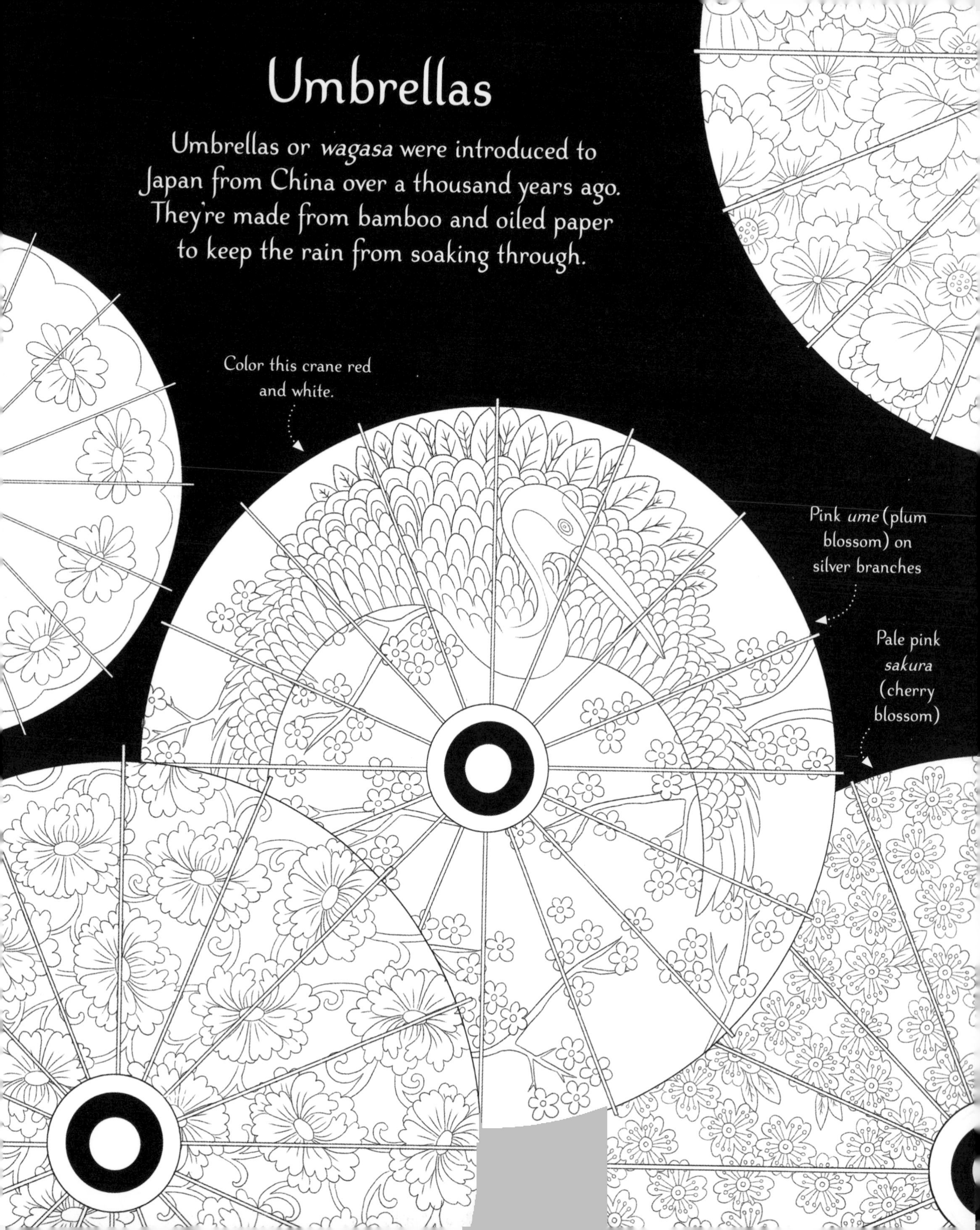

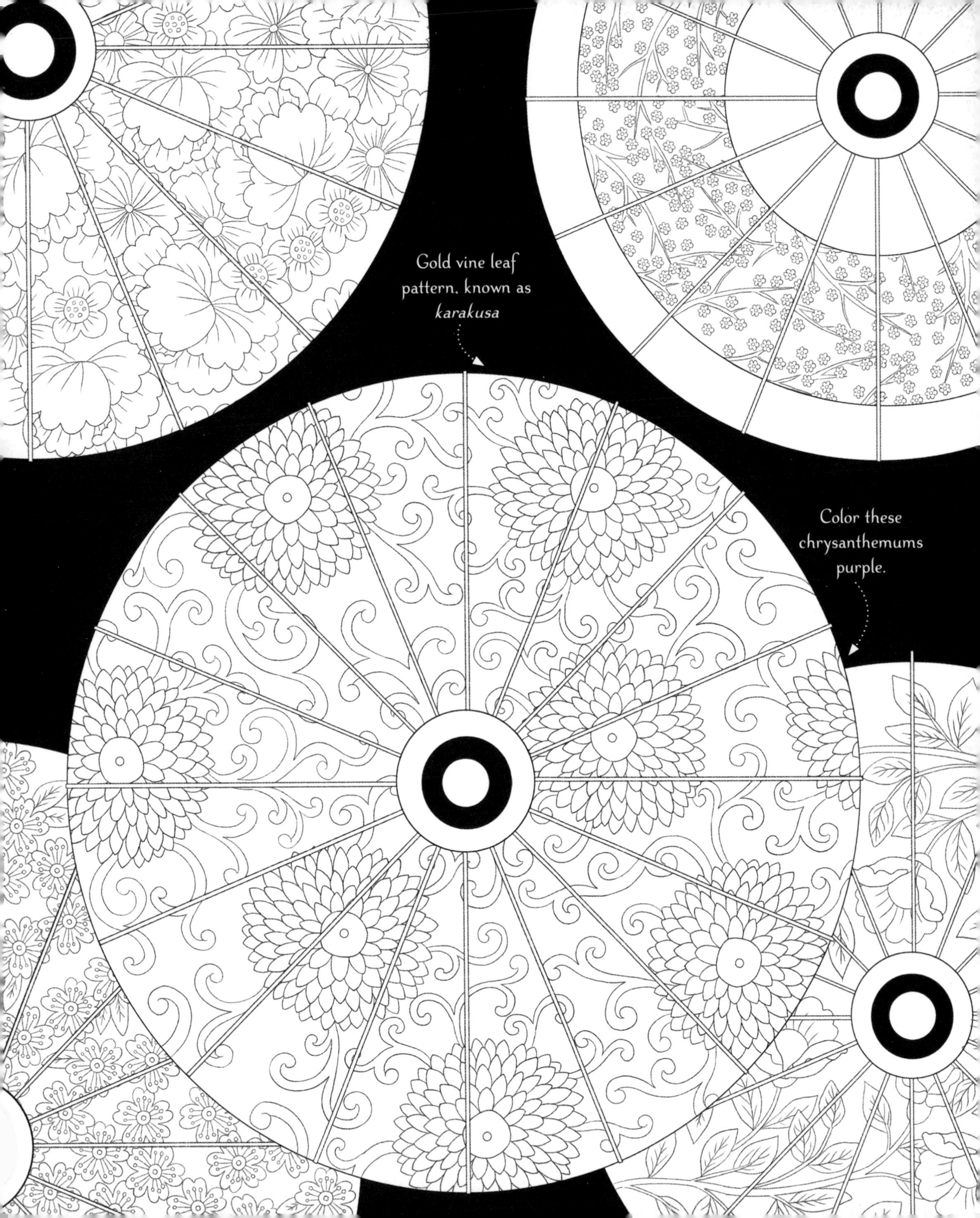
Gold vine leaf pattern, known as *karakusa*
Color these chrysanthemums purple.

Elegant accessories

Traditional Japanese accessories are made from wood, silk, precious metals and tortoiseshell. *Hana kanzashi* are fabric hair accessories that look like flowers and are worn for different seasons and festivals.

Opposite page: a *maiko* (trainee *geisha*) with *kanoko dome*, an elaborate hair accessory

Wooden hair stick and comb named *kogai* and *kushi*, worn on special occasions, such as weddings

Chrysanthemum *hana kanzashi* are worn by *maikos* in October. Color them pink and red.

This box is used for makeup and can be tied to an *obi*.

Fabulous fans

Folding fans, named *sensu*, made of silk, paper or sandalwood, were invented over a thousand years ago.

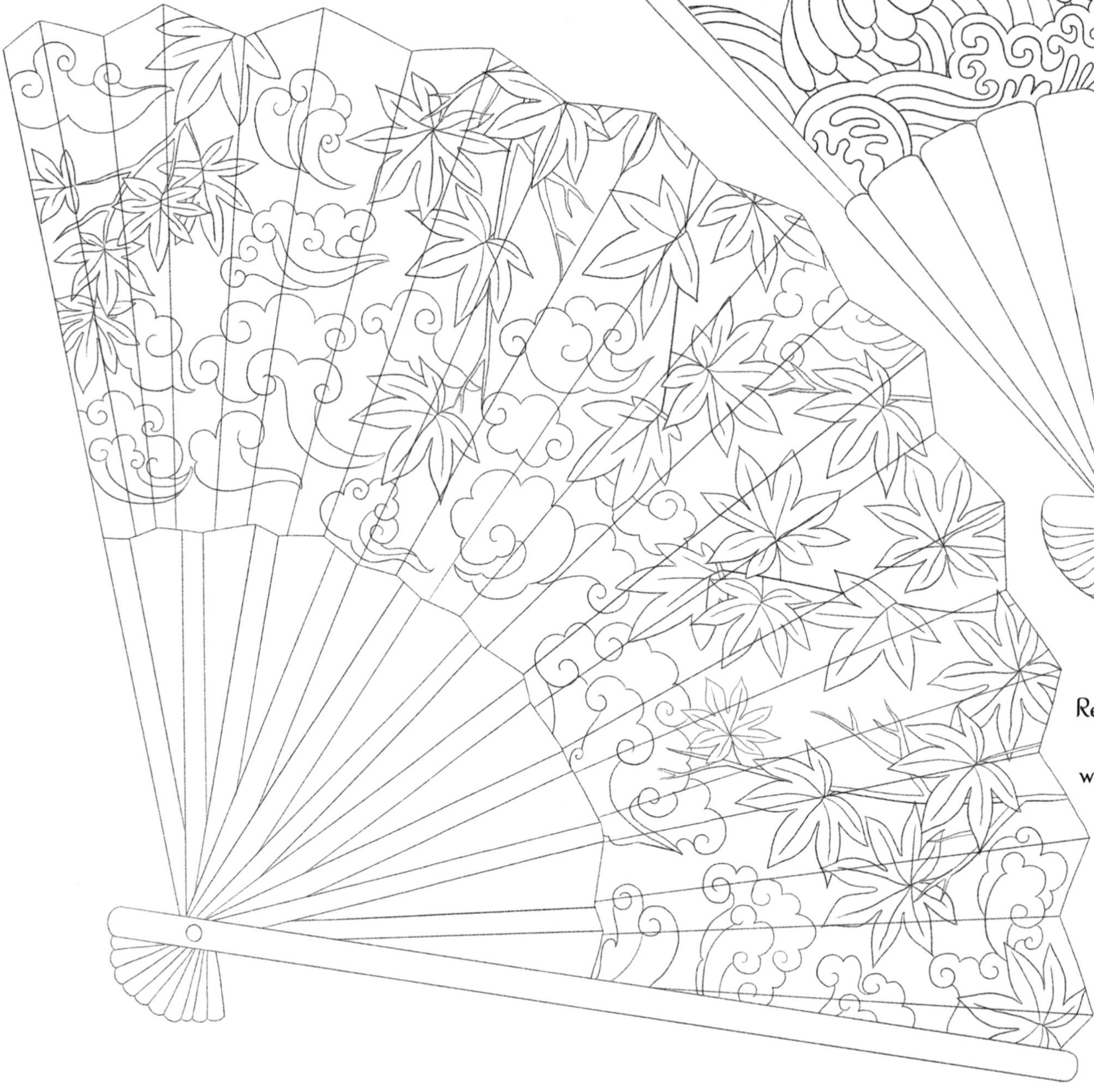

Red maple leaves are fall and winter patterns.

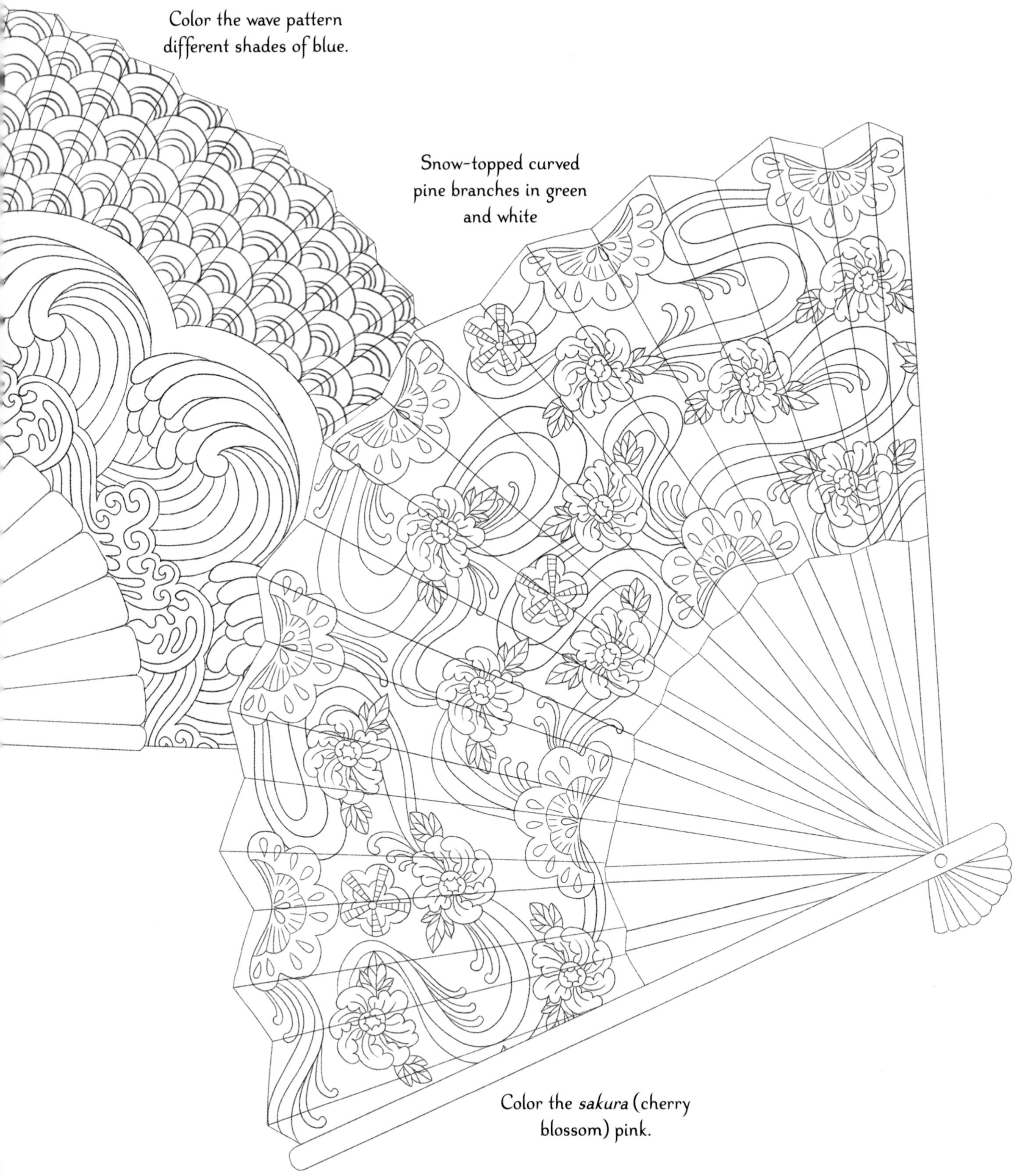

Color the wave pattern different shades of blue.

Snow-topped curved pine branches in green and white

Color the *sakura* (cherry blossom) pink.

Paper folding

Paper folding, sometimes known as *origami*, is a traditional Japanese craft, first used for religious ceremonies in the 6th century. Now people make all sorts of things – birds, butterflies and flowers.

Blue waves and pink *ume* (plum blossom) cover this butterfly.

Color the fans half green and half red.

This paper flower is decorated with *ume* (plum blossom). Color the petals yellow and the leaves green.

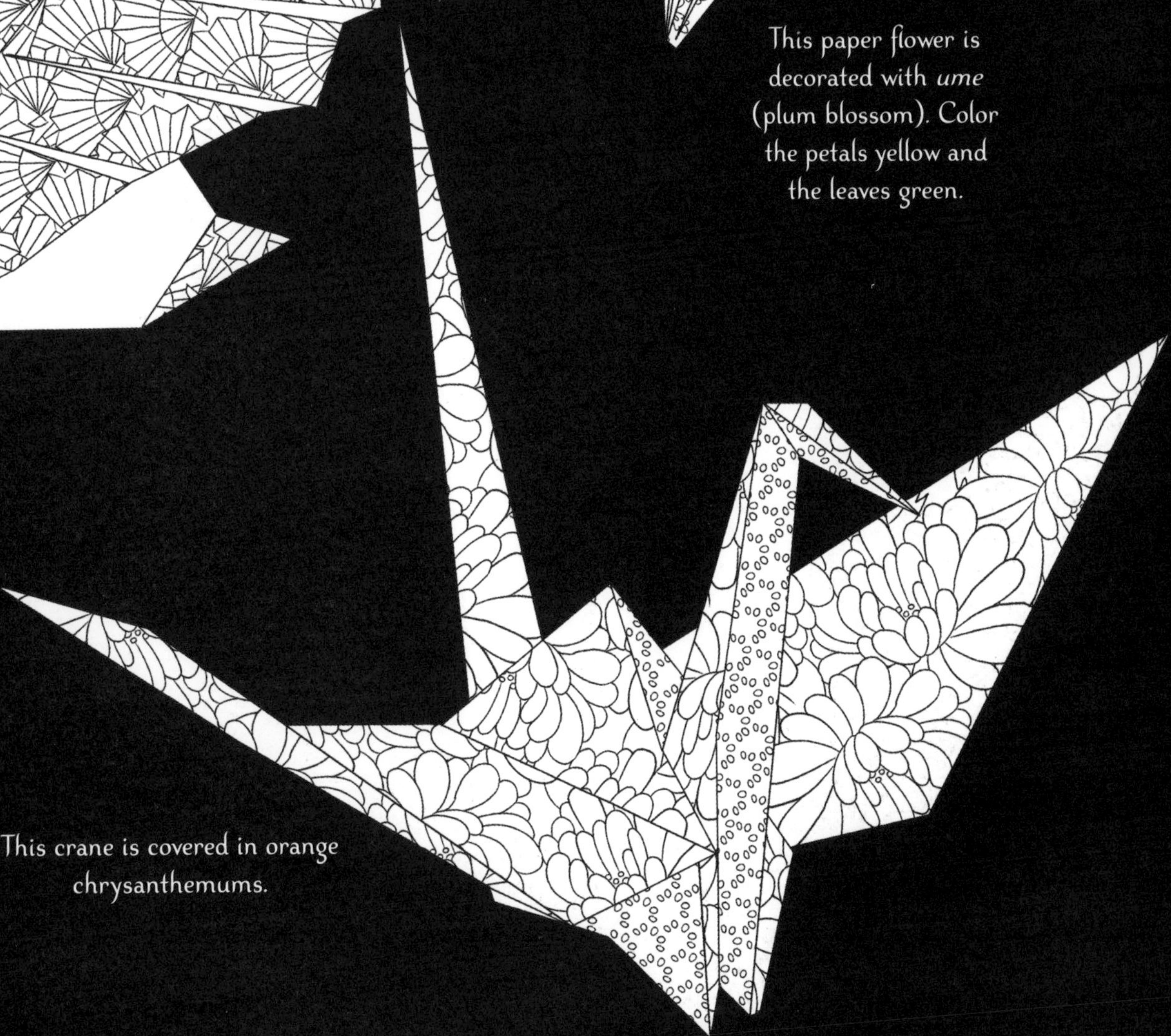

This crane is covered in orange chrysanthemums.

Stencil decoration

Fabric decorated with stencils is named *bingata*. It is used for *kimonos* and other clothing. It requires many stages to create the finished pattern, using rice paste, paints and dyes.

Kokeshi dolls

These wooden dolls, known as *kokeshis*, were traditionally made in northern Japan. Each town had its own style of *kokeshi.*

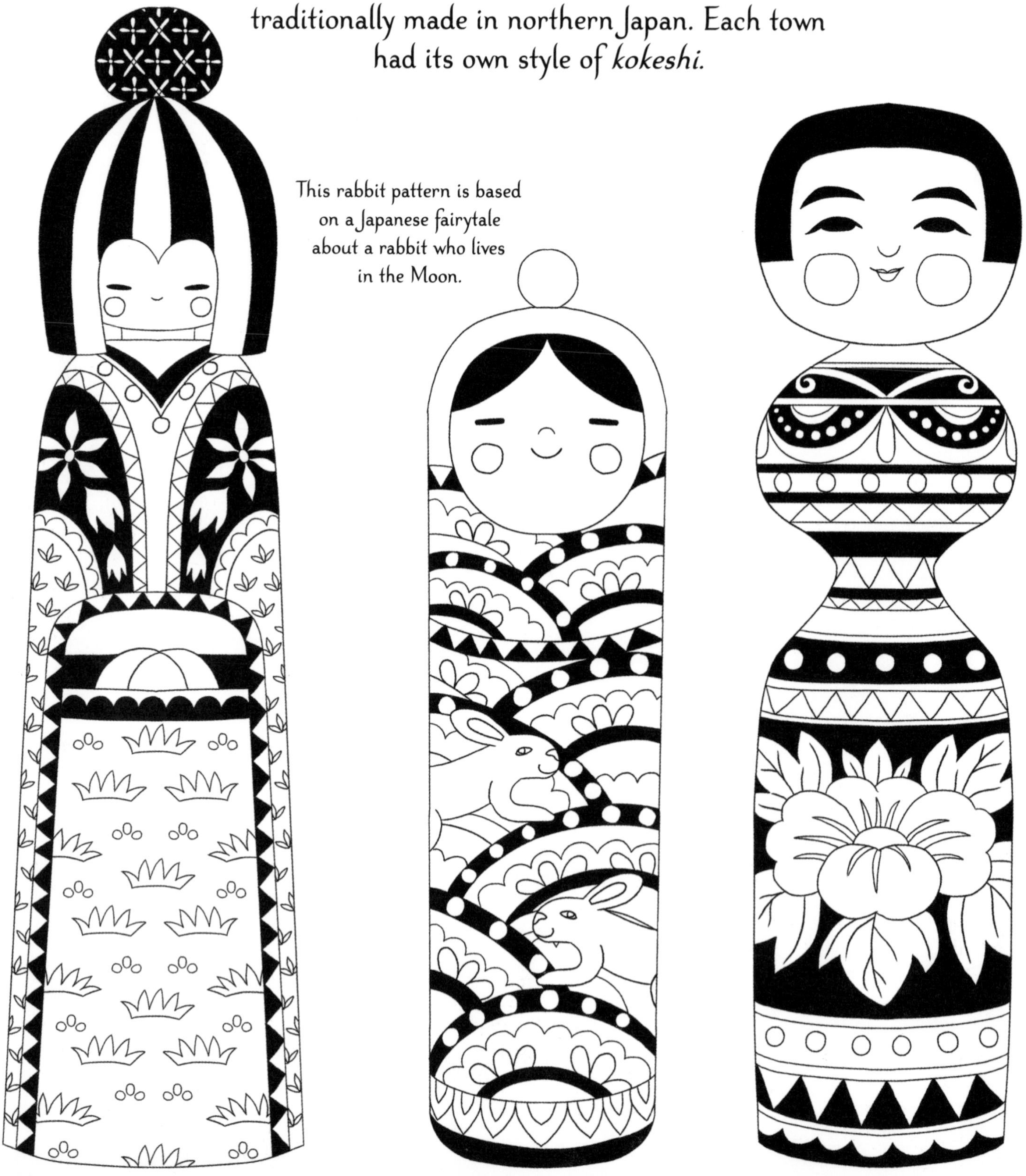

This rabbit pattern is based on a Japanese fairytale about a rabbit who lives in the Moon.

Traditional *kokeshis* are handpainted. Color this one in traditional *kokeshi* colors – red, yellow and purple.

Color the flower patterns on this *kokeshi* yellow and orange.

This little *kokeshi* has red cheeks and a maple leaf pattern on its *kimono.*

Colorful ceramics

There are many styles of Japanese ceramics. The vase on the left is decorated using gold wire. The other things here are from Arita, a town famous for its porcelain.

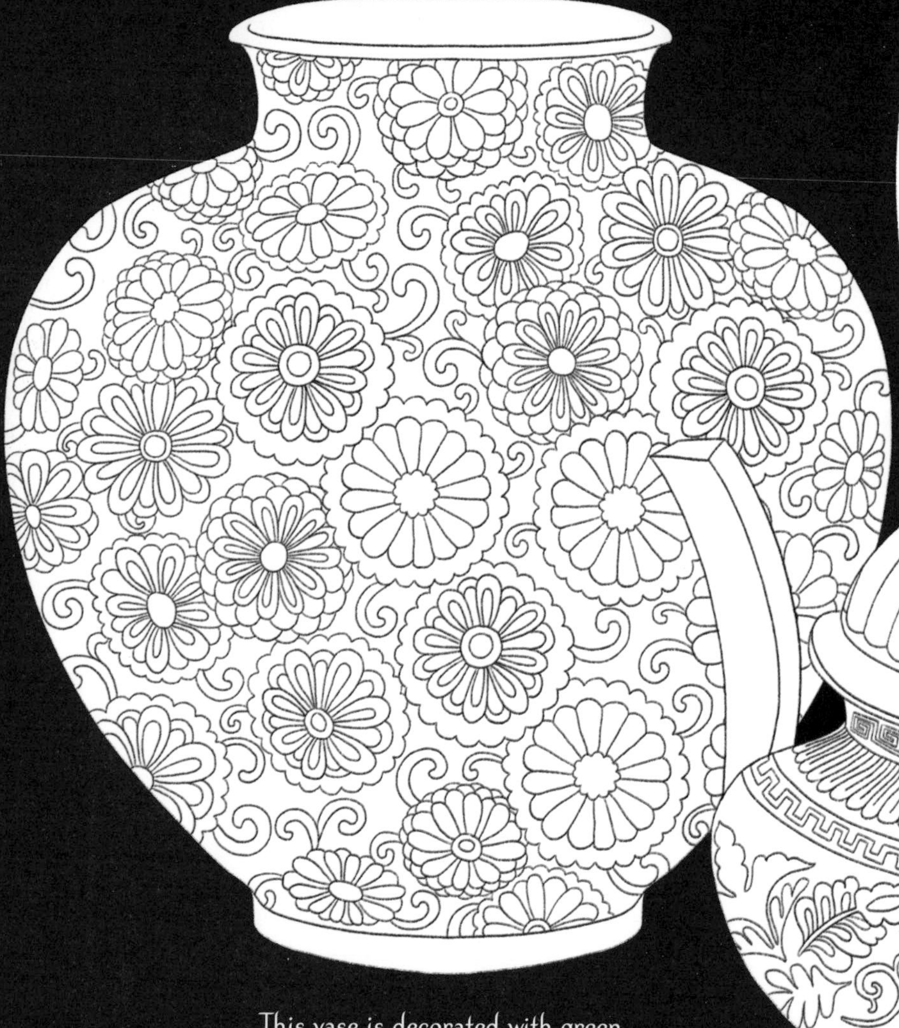

This vase is decorated with green *karakusa* (vine leaves) and red and yellow flowers.

In Japan, peacocks are a symbol of love and kindness. They are brightly colored in blue, green and gold.

Woodblock prints

Woodblock printing is an old Japanese craft. Shapes are carved into blocks of wood, dipped in ink, then pressed onto paper. Traditional prints were often of beautiful women, actors, nature, and scenes from Japanese history and legends.

In this print, two men perform a traditional dance for a spring festival using a lion costume, called *shishi-mai.* Color the lion's head red. The women are watching the dance, but also looking at the pink *sakura* (cherry blossom).

Japanese patterns

All the patterns on the next few pages are based on designs found on Japanese fabrics, clothing, ceramics, papers and paintings. Look for chrysanthemum, crane and carp patterns.

Usborne Quicklinks

For links to websites where you can find out more about Japanese designs and patterns, and see lots more examples, go to the Usborne Quicklinks website at www.usborne.com/quicklinks and enter the keywords "Japanese patterns". Please follow the internet safety guidelines at the Usborne Quicklinks website.

Edited by Emily Bone. First published in 2016 by Usborne Publishing, Usborne House, 83-85 Saffron Hill, London EC1N 8RT, England. www.usborne.com

AE. First published in America 2016.